C000262832

HIND
Hans-Heiri Stapfer

Front cover illustration:
Mi-24D 'Red 574' executes a low pass over Budaörs in June 1987. This helicopter is equipped with the 'Natasha Device' for ground-to-air missile warning, a system developed in response to combat experience in Afghanistan and now standard equipment for all WarPac Mi-24s. (Walter Hodel)

Back cover illustrations:
Top:
An early Mi-24D of the Hungarian Air Force at Budaörs, June 1988. The AT-2 'Swatter' missile rails are typical equipment for the 'Hind-D' and a common feature of the later 'Hind-E'. The IRCM jammer is missing here, although its mounting is present.

Bottom:
Ground crewman load Mi-24D 'Black 490' with Type S-5 rockets; the rear sections of the UB-32 pods have been removed for the purpose. AT-2 'Swatter' missiles are also carried. This photograph was taken on 29 August 1985 at a public display at Holzdorf, home base for the MiG-21MF-equipped *Jagdfliegergeschwader 1 'Fritz Schmenkel'*.

1. An Mi-24VS ('Hind-E') in flight over an Afghan city. The Mi-24 became the best-known (and most notorious) aircraft used by the Soviet occupation forces during the conflict. It saw extensive service in Afghanistan, as well as in the Iran-Iraq war, in Central Africa, and in Nicaragua against the US-sponsored Contra rebels.

Mi-24 HIND

Hans-Heiri Stapfer

ARMS AND
ARMOUR

2. Maintenance work on 'White 13', an early Mi-24D. Like all Soviet helicopters, the 'Hind' is easy to maintain and the machine is reliable even in bad weather. The hinged panels covering the Isotov TV-3-117 powerplant also serve as maintenance platforms. Early Mi-24s had a rounded cover over the nose-mounted air data boom, replaced on later versions of the 'Hind' by a cross-shaped cover.

INTRODUCTION

st published in Great Britain in
90 by Arms and Armour Press,
iers House, 41-47 Strand,
ndon WC2N 5JE.

stributed in the USA by Sterling
olishing Co. Inc., 387 Park
enue South, New York, NY
016-8810.

stributed in Australia by
oricorn Link (Australia) Pty. Ltd,
). Box 665, Lane Cove, New
uth Wales 2066. Australia.

Arms and Armour Press, 1990

rights reserved. No part of this
ok may be reproduced or
nsmitted in any form or by any
eans electronic or mechanical
luding photocopying recording
any information storage and
rieval system without
rmission in writing from the
olisher.

tish Library Cataloguing in
blication Data
apfer, Hans-Heiri
-24 Hind
 Military helicopters
Title II. Series
3.746047
3N 1-85409-063-1

ne drawings by Robert
etzyngier.

signed and edited by DAG
blications Ltd. Designed by
vid Gibbons; edited by Roger
esneau; layout by Cilla Eurich;
eset by Typesetters
rmingham) Ltd. and Ronset
pesetters Ltd.; camerawork by
&E Reproductions, North
mbridge, Essex; printed and
und in Great Britain by The
den Press, Oxford.

The Mi1 Mi-24 'Hind' is without doubt the best-known Soviet helicopter. It was the first dedicated gunship to be designed in the Soviet Union and the first to feature a retractable undercarriage, enabling it to reach speeds of nearly 200mph (320kph). The Mi-24 has seen action in the Iran-Iraq war, in the Nicaraguan conflict and, of course, in Afghanistan. The Afghan war, like Vietnam for the Americans, has had a tremendous influence on the development of Soviet helicopters in general and on the Mi-24 in particular.

The origins of the Mi-24 go back to 1966, when the Soviet Government issued a requirement for a dedicated helicopter gunship. The Mil design bureau approached the challenge in a typical Russian manner, using components modified from proven designs; the main rotor, for example, was adapted from that fitted to the well-established Mi-8 'Hip'. The first prototype flew in 1969 under the designation V-24, and following the completion of factory and state acceptance trials this machine was approved for production, as the Mi-24, at the State Aircraft Factories at Arsenyev and Rostov. The first operational machine was delivered to the Soviet Air Force during 1972.

In spring 1973 the first Mi-24s were deployed to the German Democratic Republic as part of the Group of Soviet Forces Germany (GSFG), where, for the first time, startled NATO officers were able to observe the new gunship. NATO's Air Standards Coordinating Committee (ASSC) gave it the name 'Hind'; the production Mi-24 was code-named 'Hind-A', while one of the pre-series V-24s was coded 'Hind-B' since its existence was not reported until after that of the production aircraft had become known. The code-name 'Hind-C' was issued for a training variant which lacked the AT-2 'Swatter' missile rails and the Afanasyev A-12.7 nose gun of the 'Hind-A'.

The 'Hind-A' was also deployed to Afghanistan, where the type saw considerable combat for the first time. The absence of a factory designation means that the first production variant of the 'Hind' is known simply as the Mi-24A in Soviet and Warsaw Pact (WarPac) regiments, adopting the suffix 'A' from the NATO ASCC name 'Hind-A'. A much modified variant followed, retaining the rotor head, transmission and basic airframe of the 'Hind-A' but incorporating a new nose section with the pilot and weapons systems operator (WSO) housed in a stepped, tandem cockpit with separate canopies for each crewman. The entire section was heavily armoured, creating what was in effect an armoured 'bath-tub', which offered considerably greater protection for the crew than the early 'greenhouse' cockpit. As these new helicopters appeared in East Germany, the ASCC name 'Hind-D' was allocated, and this variant became known as the Mi-24D in WarPac parlance. This was the first model of the 'Hind' to be supplied by the Soviet Union to its WarPac allies, all of which (except Romania) now operate the type; the first examples were transferred to Poland and the GDR in 1979.

Combat experience in Afghanistan showed that the Mi-24 was very vulnerable to the American Stinger ground-to-air missile with its infra-red (IR) homing seeker. As a result, a chaff/flare dispenser has been fitted to the tail boom and an infra-red countermeasures (IRCM) jammer aft of the engine housing. A further modification has seen infra-red suppression boxes fitted to redesigned exhaust outlets in order to reduce the temperature of the hot gases; mixed with cold air in this way, the gases are diverted into the wash of the main rotor, where their temperature is further reduced in the air flow.

A missile warning device has recently been developed for 'Hind'. This is a sophisticated system which can distinguish all missile types that may pose a threat and also provides the pilot with bearing and range data. The warning is audible, provided by a computerized female voice speaking through the intercom, and the system is generally known as the 'Natasha Device' by Soviet personnel. The presence of the 'Natasha Device' is indicated by two nose sensors on both sides of the WSO's cockpit and by a further warning sensor on the tail, above the position light.

The export designation for the Mi-24D is Mi-25, and, to date, sixteen countries outside WarPac have received the helicopter (with avionics downgraded, according to customer). An almost parallel development to the Mi-24D has been the Mi-24 'Hind-E'. This variant differs from the 'Hind-D' in having new stub-wing endplates designed to accommodate the tube-launched 'Spiral' missile (first tested operationally in 1974) and an enlarged radar guidance pod on the port side of the nose. The first Mi-24s with the AT-6 'Spiral' equipment were seen by NATO in East Germany in 1979, and it was then that the reporting named 'Hind-E' was allocated. At the time or writing, the AT-6 has virtually replaced the AT-2 'Swatter' in Soviet regiments.

The Afghan War also demonstrated that in high altitudes and hot climates the Mi-24's ceiling was poor and needed to be improved; as a result, a new version of the Isotov TV-3-117 powerplant, the TV-3-117V, was introduced, which enhanced the aircraft's performance considerably in such regimes. This 'Hind' model received the designation Mi-24VS, and it was followed by the Mi-24VE with minor internal improvements. Both the Mi-24VS and the Mi-24VE are externally indistinguishable from the Mi-24E, so no other ASCC reporting name was allocated; within WarPac regiments both variants are referred to simply as the Mi-24V (for *Visotny*, or Altitude). The Mi-24VS/VE is exported under the designation Mi-35 and, as with the Mi-25, the avionics are sometimes downgraded. Mi-35s have been exported to Afghanistan and India.

In order to improve the 'Hind's internal armament, the four-barrelled 12.7mm 'Gatling' type gun in the nose has been replaced by a twin-barrelled GSh-2-30 cannon fitted to the starboard side of the nose. While the 12.7mm weapon was effective in

3. A pre-production Mil V-24 'Hind-B' on a test flight in 197 These early gunships lacked endplates on their stub wings for the AT-6 missile and did n therefore, carry radar guidance pods beneath.

suppressing enemy troops when friendly troops were being landed, the 30mm GSh-2-30 can penetrate lightly armoured vehicles. The Soviet designation for the cannon-armed version of the 'Hind' is Mi-24P (for *Pushka*, or Cannon) and the modified machine was first observed by NATO during Exercise 'Friendship 82', when the reporting name 'Hind-F' was allocated. Most Mi-24Ps now also have the improved Isotov TV-3-117V engine, but to date none of these helicopters has been exported outside the Soviet Union.

When the Soviets began to equip their 'Hind-E's with additional tanks on the stub-wing pylons, it was first thought by Western observers that these tanks were for chemical agents which could be sprayed over troop concentrations, and the ASCC name 'Hind-G' was issued; once it became clear that no such chemicals were carried, however, the suffix 'G' was allocated to an electronic countermeasures (ECM) variant of the Mi-24V, with the low-light-level TV (LLLTV) and AT-6 'Spiral' radar pods on the nose, along with the AT-6 launch rails on the stub wings, replaced by ECM gear.

The 'Hind' caused much consternation in NATO circles after its appearance in spring 1973, so much so that it was unofficially referred to as 'The Bogeyman'. However, the design has a number of shortcomings. Its size, for example, produces a large radar signature, making it easy to detect and track with radar-guided anti-aircraft weapons, and also penalizes manoeuvrability at low speeds. In contrast to the Mi-8 'Hip', the 'Hind' is demanding to fly, earning it the nickname 'Winged Tin' in WarPac regiments. Furthermore, the 'Hind's peacetime attrition rate has been much higher than that of the 'Hip', although this contrasts sharply with the figures for losses in combat, where those for the Mi-24 are much lower than those for the Mi-8. Afghan pilots are reputedly undisciplined but brilliant: there are some, in the famous 377th Helicopter Regiment 'Hero of the Revolution', who have experienced Stinger attacks on no fewer than seven occasions and have not been shot down. In the hands of an experienced pilot, the Mi-24 is an excellent weapon.

Over 3,500 Mi-24s of all marks have been built thus far, and it is expected that production will soon be phased out in favour of the new Mi-28 'Havoc' gunship. However, to NATO's discomfort, the type will remain in service well into the next century.

Hans-Heiri Stapfer

The training version of the -24A received the NATO orting name 'Hind-C'. It was ed with endplates to the stub gs but not with AT-2 missile ls or the 12.7mm nose gun. e two Mi-24s in the back-und are standard 'Hind-As'.

▲5

▲6 ▼7

5. 'Yellow 02', an early Mi-2[?] with two TV-2-17 engines. T[he] 'Hind-A' is camouflaged in t[he] early 'cloverleaf' scheme, in [use] until the late 1970s. The co[lours] are medium green over ligh[t] grey uppersurfaces, with national markings in red an[d] white. Mi-24As did not carry national insignia on the undersurfaces.

6. The first 'Hinds' supplied [to] the Afghan Air Force were M[i-] 24Bs. This example, 'Black 3[?]' has dust guards fitted in fro[nt of] the main intakes and olive green paintwork overspraye[d] with sand colour; the undersurfaces are light blue[.] The AT-2 'Swatter' rails and camera on the inboard wing pylon are missing from this machine. (W. Luczak)

7. Two Mi-24Bs at low level[,] the normal operating altitud[e] for 'Hind' pilots. The machi[ne] on the left carries the tactica[l] number 28 in yellow; that o[n] the right has 23 in the same colour.

8. The WSO's cockpit in an Mi-24A. Despite the control stick, the opportunities for the WSO to fly the helicopter are limited. The console on the right contains switches for weapons operation. The instrument panel and consoles are black, the general interior finish chromate green. The early 'greenhouse' offered little protection against ground fire.

8▲

9. An Mi-24B with the 'greenhouse' cockpit. In contrast to the later Mi-24D, the 'Hind-A' had a fully retractable nose undercarriage, closed by doors. (Dusan Mikolas)

9▲   10▼

10. An Mi-24A with its A-12.7 nose gun removed. This weapon was operated by the WSO and was intended to pin down enemy troops while friendly troops were landed. Armour plating was fitted beneath the cockpit glazing, but in general the standards of protection against small-arms fire were poor. In the Mi-24A the WSO sat in the front cockpit, with the pilot and flight engineer side by side behind him.

▲11 ▼12

13.▲

11. A formation of early Mi-24Ds, lacking the debris guards in front of the engine intakes. 'Yellow 04', nearest the camera, is camouflaged in light brown and earth brown, with pale blue undersurfaces. The nose booms of early Mi-24Ds were not fitted with low-speed sensors.

12. The first two Mi-24Ds supplied to Poland. These gunships carry the serial numbers 1015 and 1016, the last two digits of which are applied in white on the tail boom. Both aircraft feature the early-pattern VHF mast. Polish Mi-24Ds were shown to the public for the first time on 27 June 1979.

13. Three Mi-24Ds take off for a training flight. None of these machines has the chaff/flare dispenser or the IRCM jammer.

14. A close-up view of the four-barrelled 'Gatling' type 12.7mm gun. It has a rate of fire of about 4,000 rounds a minute and a maximum effective range of some 4,000ft (1,200m). The cyrillic inscription on the ammunition access doors means 'Charge 24 (volts)'. The blister below the pitot tube is a radar warning antenna; the device on the left is the LLLTV (the armoured doors for the TV camera are usually kept closed); and the pod at lower right is the director for the AT-2 'Swatter' missiles (the 'Hind-E's AT-6 pod is larger, and rounded in section).

15. Three 'Hind' crews hold a briefing in front of Mi-24D 'White 15'. All wear the VKK-6 flying suit and the flight helmet introduced in 1982. On some training missions only the pilot and WSO fly in the helicopter, although the standard crew comprises also a flight engineer.

14.▲　　**15.▼**

16. Mi-2 'Hoplite' 'White 4311' undergoes maintenance; in the background is Mi-24 'White 14' A number of Mi-2s have been assigned to Mi-24 units for liaison and scouting duties. The rotor blades of the Mi-24 are normally grey with a silver leading-edge strip; the interior surfaces of the engine covers, which serve also as work platforms, are chromate green. The Mi-2 is built in Poland by WSK Swidnik.

17. An Mi-24D of *Kampf-hubschraubergeschwader 57 'Adolf von Lützow'*, based at Basepohl in the northern GDR. This unit, the first assault unit created in the East German Air

rce, is equipped with both the
-8TBK and the Mi-24D, and
ack 403' was one of the first
nds' it received; note the
ly VHF antenna mast. These
nd-Ds' were originally
ished in light grey and
dium green, with light blue
dersurfaces, but these colours
re later changed to the
ndard European scheme of
ht green and medium green.

. An early Mi-24D, 'Black
09' takes off as a MiG-23BN
ogger' flies overhead. The
echs use four-digit tactical
mbers painted in black and
nly outlined in white, with
all, white-outlined national
rkings. The Russian *'Opasno'*
l warning on its yellow
ckground is retained however;
ngary, Poland and the GDR
play these notices in their
n languages.

18▲

. A close-up photograph of
e AT-2 'Swatter' missile rails.
ere are considerable
fferences between the AT-2
d AT-6 systems, since the
tter are tube-launched. The
ub wings (which contribute up
24 per cent of the total lift at
gh speeds, and also reduce the
rn radius) each have
rdpoints for two pylons.
stead of the UB-32 pod,
mbs of up to 250kg (550lb)
d the UPK-23 gunpod
rrying a twin-barrelled 23mm
nnon can be fitted. The blister
the centre of the endplate is a
sition light; that in front is
rt of the radar warning
stem.

19▲   20▼

. Ground crewmen examine a
ir of UB-32 rocket pods. Each
d can accommodate 32
llow-charge, unguided Type
5 57mm rockets, effective
m 900 to 4,500ft and having
velocity of about 1,500fs. The
wer portion of the pylon is,
pically, silver, while the wing
dersurfaces are pale blue. The
wer half of the pylon is a
iversal mounting which can
cept both the UB-16-57U and
e UB-32 pod, and it is also
stalled on the Mi-8/17 'Hip'
licopter, all Sukhoi 'Fitters',
e MiG-21 'Fishbed' and the
G-23 'Flogger'.

21. An early-production Mi-24D, 'Black 406' of the East German Air Force, seen here hovering at Basepohl. This aircraft carries a 'winged Q' badge just below the pilot's cockpit, equivalent to the Sov[iet] 'Otlitshnij Samoljot' and indicating that the machine s[o] adorned is in first-class condition. The badge is award[ed] to aircraft and helicopters whi[ch] serve a required number of trouble-free flight-hours.

22. East German troops engaged in camouflaging a pai[r] of Mi-24Ds during Exercise 'Soujus 81', held in March and April 1981 in the GDR. The canopies are first covered by tarpaulins to prevent glint, the[n] the entire airframes will be shrouded in camouflage nettin[g]

▲21   ▼22

3. This Polish Mi-24D, 'White
4', is a later variant, with the
revised VHF antenna; the 'Hind-
' in the background, 'White
3', is an early model. All these
helicopters lack the IRCM pod
and chaff/flare dispenser and are
painted in the standard
European camouflage of light
green and medium green.

4. An Mi-24 'Hind-D' at the
hover. From the front, the
'Hind' looks quite menacing,
and its size does nothing for the
morale of enemy troops: the
effect is similar to that of the
sirens fitted to Stuka dive-
bombers during the Second
World War. However, the large
size and the awesome
appearance of the Mi-24 have
disadvantages: the gunship has
a big radar signature and is not
particularly manoeuvrable at
low speeds.

23▲   24▼

25. WSO, pilot and flight engineer board an Mi-24 'Hind-D'. Intensive and prolonged training is required to enable crew members to handle this big helicopter properly. It operates at very low altitudes at speeds of up to 155mph (250kph) – even in bad weather. To guide an AT-2 missile with a joystick also calls for a good deal of training since the 'Hind' is notorious for its vibration. The 'Hind' is much more difficult for crews to cope with than, for example, the Mi-8 'Hip', and peacetime attrition rates reflect this.

26. A formation of Polish Mi-24s, each differing slightly from the others in configuration. 'White 77' is a mid-production 'Hind-D' with the new VHF antenna; 'White 57' has the IRCM jammer on the engine fairing and the chaff/flare dispenser beneath the tail; 'Red 13' is a very early Mi-24D with the original VHF antenna and no IRCM dome or chaff/flare dispenser; and the last aircraft in the formation, 'White 56', has the same fittings as '57'.

27. The Mi-24 is the first Soviet helicopter to incorporate a retractable undercarriage, enabling the machine to reach maximum speed of 200mph (320kph). Interestingly, this concept was abandoned for follow-on gunships, and the 'Hind's successor, the Mi-28 'Havoc' cannot carry troops – another departure from the Mi-24 design.

28. A line-up of Mi-24Ds. The machine nearest the camera is 'White 74', the digits of the tactical number being repeated on the cover over the low-speed sensor (and on other 'accessories', such as the air intake and exhaust guards). The protective cover for the pitot tube is red and is tagged. The next gunship in line, 'White 1' has its entire cockpit covered khaki canvas.

29. An Mi-24D is prepared for mission; all the covers on the air data boom, the pitot head and the air intakes will be removed, and note also the guard over the pilot's windscreen wipers. The covers for the IFF antenna, pitot tube and air data boom are red, while those over the engine intakes are khaki.

▲25 ▼26

29▼

27▲ 28▼

▲30

30. An Mi-24D at its typical operational altitude, only a few feet above the tree-tops. In contrast to that of the 'Hind-A', the nose wheel of the 'D' is only semi-retractable. The blisters on the fuselage just behind the stub wings accommodate the main wheels. This gunship, with the black-painted tactical number '0147', has the new VHF aerial but no IRCM jammer or chaff/flare dispenser.

31. An Mi-24D executes a low pass at top speed. WarPac crews have nicknamed the Mi-24 the 'Winged Tin'; its handling characteristics are not outstanding, although in the control of an experienced pilot it is a very effective weapon. The Mi-24 is built at two state factories in the Soviet Union, at Rostov and at Arsenyev.

▼31

East German soldiers embark from an Mi-24D during a May 1982 exercise; as shown by the extended undercarriage legs, the helicopter is virtually hovering. The men are armed with East German-manufactured Kalashnikov rifles; the helicopter itself carries, usually, a single UB-32 pod. The glazed fuselage panels can be opened for use as firing positions, but the severe vibration would make aiming extremely difficult.

Mi-24D 'Black 4009' shortly after taking off. The 'Hind-D's take-off weight is about 24,250lb (11,000kg) and the robust undercarriage allows a rolling take-off at heavier all-up weights. One of the shortcomings of the early Isotov TV3-117 engine was its poor high-altitude performance – leading to a poor climb rate in 'hot and high' conditions – and this failing was made very evident during the Afghan War.

▲ 34

▲ 35   ▼ 36

34. Mi-24D 'Black 532', a late-production gunship with the chaff/flare dispenser and the IRCM jammer platform, the former simply strapped beneath the tail boom. There are two Mi-24 units in the East German Air Force, *Kampfhubschrauber-geschwader 57 'Adolf von Lützow'* at Basepohl and *Kampfhubschraubergeschwader 67 'Ferdinand von Schill'* at Cottbus.

35. 'Black 418', an Mi-24D equipped with a UB-32 pod on each of its outboard pylons. The fairing on the tail boom beneath the tactical number is the GIK gyrocompass unit; the two discs are white, while the interior of the bay is black. No national markings are applied to the undersurfaces of East German Mi-24s.

36. An Mi-24 pilot entering his gunship. The door interior is black and the handle white. The pilot enters the helicopter on the starboard side, the WSO from port. The black inscription on the hatch, *'Podnojka'*, means 'Foot-step'.

37. A WSO in his 'office'. The interior of the canopy framing is black, as are the front and rear of the instrument panel; the pitot tubes on each side of the glazing are natural metal. The WSO is provided with basic flying controls, but in the Afghan conflict WSOs proved to be incapable of taking over from the pilot in an emergency. In contrast to fighter pilots, Mi-24 crew members have neither ejection seats nor parachutes.

38. Pilot and WSO discuss a sortie. Both men are wearing leather handgear rather than the helmet introduced in 1982. The four-barrelled 12.7mm gun has a field of fire of about 70 degrees either side of the direction of flight, with some degrees of elevation and 60 of depression.

ЗАРЯДКА УСПУ-24

▲39 ▼40

39. A pair of Polish Mi-24Ds. For the armoured reconnaissance role, a formation of three Mi-24s is used, two flying in front with the leader behind at a higher altitude, to give protection. In the Iran-Iraq war, air-to-air combats took place between Iraqi 'Hinds' and Iranian Sea-Cobras, and on one occasion an Iraqi Mi-24 succeeded in shooting down an F-4 Phantom – the first time in history that a helicopter has brought down a jet fighter. Equipped with the GSh-2-30 cannon, the Mi-24 is very effective against enemy helicopters and slow-flying aircraft.

40. An Mi-24D, no. 1016, with its two-piece passenger door and pilot's access door open; the exhaust outlet is covered with a red-painted anti-FOD plate. The 'Hind' can carry eight fully equipped troops or an equivalent cargo. The mixed 24/Mi-8 assault helicopter regiments are usually assign Mi-2s for liaison and scoutin duties and an Mi-6 for transport.

CAMOUFLAGE AND COLOURS

CAMOUFLAGE

Hind-A: Most Mi-24As were camouflaged in light grey and medium green, with light blue undersurfaces; some were camouflaged in light brown and medium brown.

Hind-D: Early Mi-24Ds were painted light grey and medium green on the upper surfaces, and light blue on the undersurfaces. This scheme was subsequently replaced by a camouflage of light green and medium green, with light blue undersurfaces. In the late 1970s, the 'cloverleaf' camouflage was in fashion, comprising a light green ground with medium green over. The 1978 camouflage scheme saw the light grey or light green replaced by tan. Those Hinds operating in Soviet Asia and Afghanistan wore Asian camouflage of tan and medium green, with light blue undersurfaces.

Hind-E/F: Light green and medium green, with light blue undersurfaces, on European and WarPac machines; tan and medium green, with light blue undersurfaces, on Asian 'Hind-E/F'.

PAINT SCHEME

In contrast to NATO the Soviet Air Force does not have an official pattern for its MI-24s and thus every 'Hind', even each machine in the production batch, varies slightly in its pattern. Soviet regulations simply call for the uppersurfaces to be painted in two different colours.

Cockpit interior: Chromate green. Interior surfaces of pilot's and WSO's canopy are black; instrument panel and WSO's weapons console also black.

Cargo/passenger compartment: Interior painted light grey, as are the inside surfaces of the two-piece doors.

Access panels: Interior surfaces of ammunition bay panels are light blue, as are the interior of the main wheelbays and the inner surfaces of the main undercarriage doors. The nose wheel well is either chromate green or light blue. The engine bay panels, which also serve as maintenance platforms, are painted either chromate green or light grey.

Rotor: Main and tail rotor medium grey. Tail rotor has one or two red stripes at the tips.

Undercarriage: Light grey, with glossy olive green hubs.

Warning notices: The inscription on the tail is always in black on a yellow background. The cyrillic 'Opasno' marking is used by 'Hinds' serving in Czechoslovakia and Afghanistan; Polish production Mi-24Ds and all 'Hind-E's in Polish service also have Soviet-language notices, while other Mi-24Ds have the Polish 'Niebezpiecznie' warning. The lettering on Hungarian 'Hinds' is 'Vigyazz!' and on East German 'Hinds' 'Gefahr'.

National Markings: On Soviet aircraft the red star has a large white and a thin red outline. Early Mi-24 'Hind-As' had no national markings on the lower surfaces of the fuselage, but with the introduction of the Mi-24D all Mi-24s of the Soviet Air Force have had them here. National markings are painted on the undersurfaces of Afghan, Polish and Hungarian Mi-24s but not on Czech or East German machines.

Tactical numbers: The Soviet Air Force applies two-digit tactical numbers, either behind the pilot's cockpit or on the tail boom, in either white or black outlined. Czechoslovakia uses four-digit tactical numbers as thin white outlines; Hungary applies three-digit tactical numbers in red with a thin white outline; and the USSR applies three-digit numbers in black. Poland at first used two-digit tactical numbers in white but from about 1986 has introduced three-digit numbers with no outlines.

Nose gun: Barrels of guns on Mi-24 'Hind-As', 'Hind-D/Es' and 'Hind-Fs' are gunmetal.

UB pods: UB-32 pods are mainly silver, although some are painted light blue.

80mm pod: Generally silver overall, with chromate green endplates at the rear, where the missiles are loaded.

AT-2 'Swatter': Dark olive drab or, occasionally, black.

AT-6 'Spiral': Launch tubes generally painted dark olive drab.

Bombs: All Soviet bombs are dark grey. Stripes around the belly denote the charge; for example, two yellow stripes around the bomb indicate 'High Explosive'. Some Soviet bombs in Afghanistan bore English as well as cyrillic inscriptions.

UPK-23 pod: Silver overall with black stencilling. Gunmetal cannon barrel.

TECHNICAL DATA

Type	V-24	Mi-24A	Mi-24D	Mi-24VE	Mi-24P
ASCC reporting name	'Hind-B'	'Hind-A'	'Hind-D'	'Hind-E'	'Hind-F'
Length (m)	16.80	16.80	17.50	17.50	17.50
Rotor diameter (m)	17.30	17.30	17.30	17.30	17.30
Height (m)	5.97	5.97	5.97	5.97	5.97
Empty weight (kg)	8,000	8,400	8,700	8,700	8,200
Take-off weight (kg)	11,000	11,000	11,000	12,000	12,000
Maximum speed (kph)	300	320	320	320	335
Cruising speed (kph)	250	250	250	270	270
Ceiling (m)	4,500	4,500	4,500	4,500	4,500
Range (km)	310	310	310	450	450
Engine (Isotov)	TV-2-117	TV-2-117	TV-3-117	TV-3-117V	TV-3-117V
Emergency rating (hp)	1,500	2,200	2,200	2,200	2,200
Gun armament	–	A-12.7	YakB	YakB	GSh-2-30
Missiles	–	AT-2	AT-2	AT-6	AT-6
External armament	UB-16/32	UB-32 FAB 250	UB-32 FAB 250	UB-32 FAB 250 UPK-23 Napalm	UB-32 FAB 250 UPK-23 Napalm
Crew	3	3	3	3	3
Passengers/ troops	8	8	8	8	8

'HIND' VARIANTS

V-24 'Hind-B': Prototype; pre-production Mil designs have the prefix 'V' (*Vertoljot* or Helicopter). Early pre-production Mi-24s had small stub wings, to accommodate two pylons each, but no endplates for anti-tank missiles.

Mi-24A 'Hind-A': First production variant, with 'greenhouse' cockpit canopy. Early Mi-24As had a pusher tail rotor to starboard side. Lacking an official designation for this variant, Soviet and allied regiments adopted the 'A' letter from the ASCC reporting name.

Mi-24B 'Hind A': improved variant with the tail rotor changed to a tractor unit to the port side, plus some minor detail changes.

Mi-24 'Hind-C': Based on the 'Hind-A', this variant has neither AT-2 'Swatter' missile rails nor A-12.7 nose gun. A training variant.

Mi-24D 'Hind-D': Variant with redesigned nose to accommodate WSO and pilot in a large, heavily armoured 'bathtub'. Following operations in Afghanistan 'Hind-Ds' were progressively updated

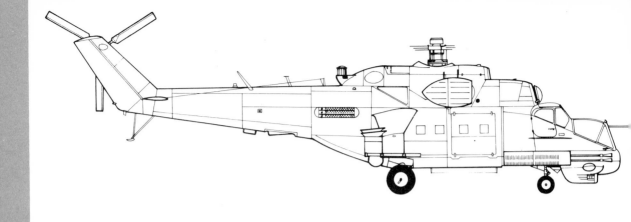

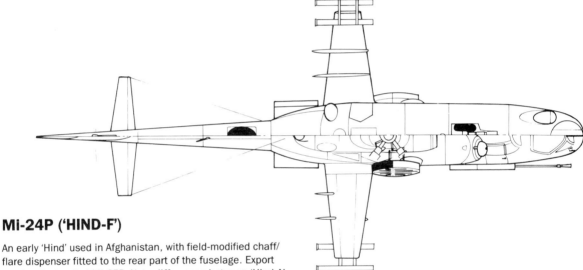

Mi-24P ('HIND-F')

An early 'Hind' used in Afghanistan, with field-modified chaff/
flare dispenser fitted to the rear part of the fuselage. Export
version designated Mi-35P. Note differences between 'Hind-A'
and 'Hind-D' as follows:

'Hind-A'

Nose section:
'Greenhouse' cockpit with
fully retractable nose wheel
and cover doors; crew access
via main doors either side of
fuselage; single-barrelled
12.7mm gun.

'Hind-D'

(D and F) New 'bathtub' type
cockpit; nose wheel semi-
retractable with no doors;
crew access via individual
doors. 'Hind-D' also fitted with
air-data boom on nose. 'Hind-
D/E' has Gatling-type YakB
12.7mm gun. 'Hind-F' has
twin GSh-2-30 (30mm)
cannon on starboard side
whereas 'Hind-D' had but one
12.7mm Gatling-type.

Tail rotor:
First version (designated Mi-
24A in Soviet service) had
rotor on starboard side; later,
more numerous versions
(designated Mi-24B) on port
side.

(D/F) Tail rotor on port side.

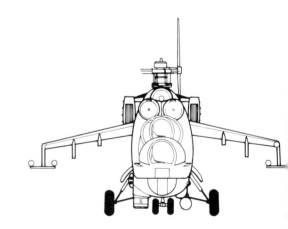

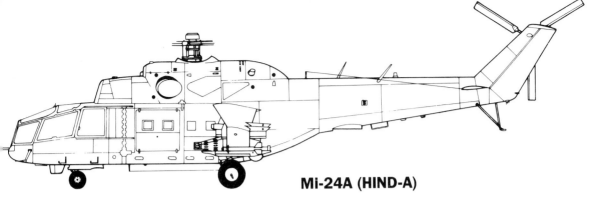

Mi-24A (HIND-A)

The first production variant of the 'Hind', with the tail rotor on the starboard side.

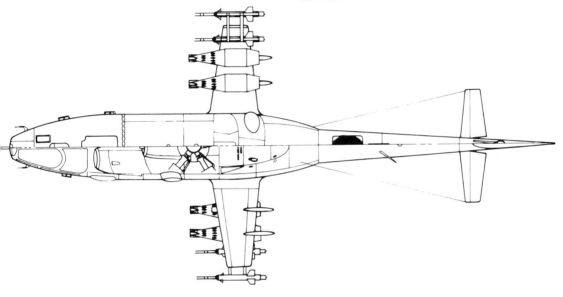

haff/flare dispenser:
ot fitted.

nfra-red suppression units:
ot fitted.

(D/F) Most retrofitted, on tail. Note that drawing shows field-modified fitment on rear half of fuselage, unique to Afghanistan.

Introduced after combat experience in Afghanistan; the hot exhaust is mixed with cold air and blown into the main rotor downwash.

Drawings by Robert Gretzyngier.

with chaff/flare dispensers, infra-red supression boxes on the exhaust stubs (to reduce exhaust temperatures) and an IRCM jammer pod on the engine fairing aft. Again lacking a designation, Soviet regiments adopted the 'D' suffix from the ASCC name and this type is thus generally referred to as the Mi-24D in Soviet and WarPac parlance.

Mi-24E 'Hind-E': Parallel development to the Mi-24D but with radar guidance pod and device on stub wing endplates to accommodate tube-launched AT-6 'Spiral' anti-tank missiles. Early Mi-24Es lacked the landing/search light on the port side but most now have it. Progressively updated as for Mi-24D.

Mi-24VS 'Hind-E': Following the Afghanistan experiences, Mi-24s displayed severe shortcomings in performance at high altitudes in hot climates. The Mi-24VS, in an effort to rectify these, was the first version of 'Hind-E' with improved power. The Mi-24VS is externally indistinguishable from the Mi-24E.

Mi-24VE 'Hind-E': Main production variant of the Mi-24, with improved high-altitude performance, developed from the Mi-24VS. Other improvements include the 'Natasha Device', a sophisticated ground-to-air missile warning device.

Mi-24P 'Hind-F': First observed in 1982, the Mi-24P (P for *Pushka*) had the swivelling nose-mounted 12.7mm MG replaced by a fixed two-barrelled GSh-2-30 cannon fitted on the starboard side.

Mi-24 'Hind G': Electronic countermeasure helicopter with the missile rails and AT-6 guidance pod deleted.

Mi-25 'Hind-D': Export variant of the Mi-24D, sometimes with downgraded electronics (depending on the customer). 'Hind-Ds' exported to WarPac countries still bear the designation Mi-24D since they are identical to those operated by the Soviet Union.

Mi-35 'Hind-E': Export variant of the Mi-24V 'Hind-E'.

Mi-35P 'Hind F': Export variant of the Mi-24P.

WEAPONS

INTERNAL

A-12.7: Fitted to Mi-24A 'Hind-A'. A single barrelled cannon with a calibre of 12.7mm.

YakB: Fitted to 'Hind-D' and 'E'. Based on the Gatling design, with four 12.7mm barrels. Rate of fire about 4,000rds/min. Operated by the WSO, it has an effective range of 1,500m. In addition to common shell and tracers, armour-piercing (AP) and high-explosive incendiary (HEI) rounds are available.

GSh-2-30: Fitted to the Mi-24P 'Hind-F'. The twin-barrelled GSh-2-30 is based on the Gast principle, where the recoil of one gun automatically loads and fires the other. The GSh-2-30 is based on the 23mm GSh-23L cannon, well proven and introduced on the MiG-21 'Fishbed' and MiG-23 'Flogger'. Rate of fire is about 3,000 rounds per minute. Fitted on the starboard side with 30mm ammunition stowed above.

EXTERNAL

UB-16-57U pod: Carried only in very limited numbers on the first Mi-24A 'Hind-As'.

UB-32 pod: Standard pod for all 'Hind-A' to 'Hind-E' variants, each pod housing 32 Type S-5 unguided rockets. The S-5 has a calibre of 57mm and weighs 8.4lb (3.8kg), with a 1.75lb (0.8kg) warhead. It has a length of 34.6in (880mm). Several warheads available, including high-explosive (HE), high-explosive incendiary (HEI) and high-explosive anti-tank (HEAT). The S-5 has now been phased out in favour of the 80mm unguided rocket.

80mm pod: Replacement for Type S-5 pod, first observed in 1986. As with Type S-5, several types of warhead are available

(HE, HEI, HEAT). The 80mm missile has a much grea penetration than the S-5; twenty per pod are fitted. Now enterin, service.

AT-2 'Swatter': Standard anti-tank weapon for 'Hind-A' and 'Hind D'. Length 3ft 11in (1.2m); weight 57.3lb (26kg); effective range 1,650–11,500ft (500–3,500m); weight of warhea 12.1lb (5.5kg). The solid-propellant radio-controlled 'Swatter' i steered in flight by means of elevons on the trailing edges of it rear-mounted cruciform wings and incorporates terminal hom ing. It is guided by a small joystick in the WSO's cockpit. Th missile must be visually tracked to the target and its operatio thus calls for a great deal of skill and training.

AT-6 'Spiral': Standard anti-tank missile for 'Hind-E' and 'Hind F' and for other operations within the Soviet Air Force an WarPac countries. First tested operationally in 1974, it is a tube-launched, second-generation, radio command-guided anti tank missile with laser homing in the terminal phase. The AT- has an improved HEAT warhead. Length 5ft 7in (1.7m); weigh about 88lb (40kg); effective range 1,650–16,500ft (500– 5,000m).

USER NATIONS

Afghanistan, Algeria, Angola, Bulgaria, Cuba, Czechoslovakia Ethiopia, German Democratic Republic, Hungary, India, Iraq Cambodia, North Korea, Libya, Nicaragua, Peru, Poland, South Yemen, Syria, Yemen, Vietnam, USA, USSR.

41. Mi-24D 'Black 485' of the East German Air Force undergoes maintenance. The 'Gatling' gun turret panelling has been removed, and a check instrument is fitted to the air data boom to test the low-speed sensors on the front. Only the port-side pitot head has been covered here.

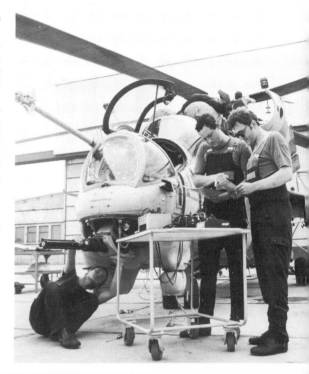

. An Mi-24D, 'Black 0147', at
ical combat altitude during a
ter exercise, necessary to
id detection by ground-based
lar. The large radar signature
oduced by the 'Hind' can be
dily tracked by most of the
st's current radar-controlled
ti-aircraft guns; these
apons may be obsolete for use
ainst fast-flying aircraft, but
y are still of value against
licopters.

42 ▲

. Polish ground crewmen
eck the rotor head of an Mi-
D. The rotor head of the TV-
117 is simple, but it is reliable
d easy to maintain. The cap is
ght grey, while the rotor
ades are medium grey with a
ver strip (the electrical de-
ing system); the head itself is
ver and the tubing black. The
tor head is the most
lnerable part of a helicopter.

43 ▲   44 ▼

. A Hungarian Mi-24D
hotographed immediately after
major overhaul, in the new
tandard camouflage scheme of
arth brown and olive drab, the
olours also used for Hungarian
iG-21s, Mi-2s and Mi-8s and
xclusive to the *Magyar Legierö*.
he tactical number, 106, is red
ith a thin white outline.
Despite the overhaul, the early-
attern exhausts have not been
eplaced by IR suppression
oxes, and neither have the
tinger warning system or the
Natasha Device' been fitted.

▲45 ▼46

Three East German Air
e Mi-24Ds fly over a
ing ground in search
ation. The first and third
opters, 'Black 530' and
k 532', are mid-production
nines in light and medium
n camouflage; that in the
re, 'Black 406', is one of the
Mi-24Ds received by the
, in light grey and medium
n paintwork and retrofitted
the chaff/flare dispenser
RCM jammer platform.
East German 'Hinds' were
revealed to the public
ng the 30th anniversary
rations on 7 October 1979,
six 'Ds' flew in formation
36 Mi-8s.

47 ▲

An Mi-24D lands to drop
troops. The strong
nwash of the rotors, clearly
here, led to the fitting of
filters in front of the main
es; they reduce power by
ten per cent but prevent
TV-3-117s from being
aged by debris: during
ations in the desert and in
dry regions such as the
lle East and Afghanistan,
could play havoc with the
nes.

An Mi-24D in the new
garian camouflage scheme
rth brown and olive drab,
light blue undersurfaces.
the large, white-outlined
onal insignia on the
erside of the fuselage. This
of national marking – the
star with a green spot
ined in white – was
oduced in 1951. It is
resting to note that during
1956 uprising the
garians adopted a national
king consisting of a red,
e and green rectangle, but
was in use for only a short
od.

A Polish Mi-24D at the
er, with undercarriage
n. This particular machine
the first Mi-24 delivered to
Polish Air Force, in 1979,
was not originally equipped
the chaff/flare dispenser on
tail boom. The serial
ber, 1014, was at first
ied as a two-digit tactical
ber, '14', later changed to
current '014' under the

48 ▲   49 ▼

three-digit system introduced by
the Polish Air Force in 1988.

49. A Polish Mi-24D, 'White 77'.
The Mi-24 is larger than might
be expected for a gunship: at
just over 55ft (16.8m) in overall
length, it is as long as a Second
World War medium bomber.
The UB-32 pods are natural
metal as are the lower halves of
the weapons pylons.

▲50   ▼51

Although still wearing the light green/medium green [cam]ouflage, this Hungarian Mi-[24] gunship is equipped with [the] redesigned exhausts to [acc]ommodate the infra-red [sup]pression boxes; the sensors [in fr]ont for the 'Natasha Device' [are] also present. As with the IR [box]es, the IRCM jammer is not [alwa]ys fitted in peacetime, [alth]ough its mounting is not [rem]oved. The new, shorter [exh]austs cause considerable [stre]aking across the rear of the [fuse]lage; this 'Hind' is [rem]arkably clean, suggesting [that] it has recently been [rele]ased following an overhaul. [(Gá]bor Szekeres)

A formation of four Mi-[24]s, all carrying the chaff/flare [disp]enser and IRCM jammer but [only] the first and third equipped [wit]h the Stinger warning radar. [In a]ddition to the two sensors [in t]he nose, there is also a [rea]r warning sensor on the tail [abo]ve the position light, as seen [on t]he aircraft nearest the [cam]era, 'White 585'. This [heli]copter also has the original [Rus]sian-language 'Opasno' tail [rea]r warning notice; the Poles [are] now leaving this notice in [Cyril]lic instead of applying the

Polish translation 'Niebez-piecznie' as on early Mi-24Ds.

52. A freshly overhauled Mi-24D, 'Red 574' of the *Magyar Legierö*, photographed over Budaörs in 1987. Note that the tail warning notice is in Hungarian – 'Vigyazz!' This 'Hind-D' is fitted with the Stinger warning device. (Urs Harnisch)

53. Two Mi-24Ds on a low pass. Only the leading 'Hind' here is equipped with the Stinger warning device and has the IRCM jammer fitted, although the other has the IRCM mounting in place.

52 ▲

53 ▼

▲54 ▼55

54. Mi-24D 'White 585' takes off, its four UB-32 pods empty. This machine is fitted with all the modifications applicable to a late-model Mi-24.

55. An Mi-24D, 'White 77', with black-painted dust guards. Behind the main wheels is a towbar, which is attached to the nose wheel for ground handling.

This machine is a mid-production variant and originally would not have been fitted with either the IRCM jammer or the countermeasures dispenser.

56. An Mi-24D on its hardstand at a Polish air base. This example is fitted with the standard UB-32 pod. The UPK-23 gunpod with twin GSh-23L cannon has recently been introduced in WarPac regiments: this rapid-fire cannon can disable lightly armoured vehicles and can also be used in air-to-air engagements.

57. An Mi-24D is towed by a STAR 660 truck to its dispersal point. The towbar, which is painted red, is identical to that used for the Mi-8 'Hip'. 'White 584' is a late-production Mi-24D. The entrance door for the passenger/cargo compartment is open, as is the pilot's access door; the WSO's canopy is closed. Note the streaking caused by the exhaust efflux.

▲58
58. Ground crewmen fit an AT-2 'Swatter' to the outboard rail of an Mi-24D. The AT-2 was the standard Soviet anti-tank missile of the late 1970s, but it has now for the most part been superseded by the AT-6 'Spiral'
▼59

in Soviet service. The AT-2 has a weight of 57lb and a span of 2ft 2in; it has a cruising speed of 335mph and an effective range of between 1,650 and 11,500ft. It can penetrate up to 500mm of rolled armour.

59. A quartet of Mi-24Ds land in a large field used as a forward operating base. The 'Hind' can carry additional AT-2 'Swatters' as well as 12.7mm ammunition boxes as cargo. All these machines have the chaff/flare

dispenser and the IRCM jammer fitted, but they do not yet have the three-digit tactical number now adopted by the Poles. Note the slight variations in the camouflage patterns of the two nearest helicopters.

60. Polish ground crewmen sort out an ammunition belt for an Mi-24's nose-mounted, four-barrelled 12.7mm gun. The AT-2 guidance pod is open; it is painted light blue on the inside, the antenna itself being black. The panel behind is also pale blue inside. For the purposes of this photograph, the number '58', in white, has been overpainted on the nose boom cover.

61. Ground crewmen load a UB-32 pod with Type S-5 rockets. The S-5 is 57mm in diameter and has a gross weight of 8.4lb; the warhead, which weighs 2.75lb, can be High-Explosive (HE), High-Explosive Incendiary (HEI) or High-Explosive Anti-Tank (HEAT). The coloured bands on the rocket denote the type of charge: the one being loaded here has a small black tip, with a yellow bank and then an orange band, then a black band. The weapons chest is olive drab outside and white inside. In order to load the S-5, the rear section of the pod has to be removed; the electrical launch system is automatically reconnected as soon as the pod is reassembled.

62. One of the two Afghan Air Force Mi-24Ds which defected to Miransha in Pakistan in July 1985. The crew of this 'Hind' were based at Khost in the District of Paktia and comprised Lt. M. Omar Noramad (pilot), his brother, and Capt. Hossain-Tan (flight engineer). At that stage of the war, Afghan pilots had not been trained to operate the 'Swatter' and their Mi-24s carried only UB-32 pods and FAB 250kg bombs for offensive sorties, as shown here. The crew reported that, on numerous occasions, these bombs and S-5 rockets failed to detonate when used in anger. (*Soldat und Technik*, via G. Lippert)

63. An Mi-24D training helicopter from the Syzran Air Force Academy, with 12.7mm gun and air data boom deleted. In this instance the nose gun position has been faired over; other Mi-24 trainers simply have the gun removed.

▲62 ▼63

4. A very early production Mi-
4E fires a tube-launched
piral' missile. The AT-6 was
rst deployed operationally in
974; it has more speed, more
nge and more accuracy than
e AT-2. This Mi-24 'Hind-E'

lacks debris guards, and neither
chaff/flare dispenser nor IRCM
jammer are fitted. The tactical
number is 'Red 33'.

65. A joint exercise involving
Mi-24Es of the Soviet Air Force

and Mi-24Ds of the Polish Air
Force. A Soviet assault regiment
includes Mi-24 and Mi-8
gunships as well as at least one
Mi-6 'Hook' for transport duties.
Mi-24E 'Yellow 08' has a
camouflage pattern of medium

green 'cloverleaf' patches over
light grey. This is an early
version of the 'Hind-E', lacking
countermeasures gear; it also
has the early-type tail rotor with
square-tipped blades.

66. An Mi-24E showing the larger, circular-section AT-6 guidance pod on the port side and the search/landing light above it. While the AT-2 pod is smaller and painted light blue overall, the front half of the AT-6 pod is in most instances black.

67. An Mi-24V, in the Asian scheme of medium green and tan, undergoes maintenance; an Mi-6 transport can be seen in the background. The 350-litre fuel tank is painted light grey. (*Soldat und Technik*, via G. Lippert)

68. A Soviet Mi-24VS taxies to take off at an Afghan base. This gunship is equipped with two 80mm pods (each holding twenty rockets) and a single AT-6 missile on each outboard station. The IR suppression kits are fitted, as is usual under wartime conditions. The AT-6 was used not only against armoured vehicles in Afghanistan but also against strongpoints and AA gun emplacements. In the background, on the right, a 'Hind-E' undergoes maintenance and a civil-registered An-12 'Cub' in Aeroflot colours can be seen.

69. An Mi-24VS 'Hind-E' crew conduct a briefing in front of their gunship; an Mi-24P 'Hind F' and an Mi-17 'Hip-H' are visible in the distance. The LLLTV pod of the 'Hind-E' differs in a number of respects from that of the 'Hind-D', for example in the latch mechanism. This 'Hind-E' is equipped with the Chrom Nik IFF antenna changed to a black type on Mi-24s produced from 1986.

▲66 ▼67

0. An Mi-24VS passes low over Kabul. This example has three chaff/flare dispensers just above the national insignia on the fuselage – an interim solution before the fitting was finally located at the end of the tail boom. The helicopter here is armed with two 'Spirals' and two 80mm pods, one of each either side.

1. Engine maintenance on an Mi-24VS in Afghanistan; note the IR suppression boxes over the exhausts. The original Isotov TV-3-117 powerplant performed poorly in the hot climate and high altitudes experienced in Afghanistan, and an improved version was therefore developed. 'Hind-Es' fitted with this modified engine are designated Mi-24V (for *Visotny*, or Altitude).

2. A detail view of an Mi-24VS serving in Afghanistan; note the three chaff/flare dispensers just behind the national insignia – a field modification. Just visible beneath the stub wing is the helicopter's full serial number,

3532421217584. The first three digits are the manufacturer's project number; the '24' stands for the military designation (Mi-24); the next four digits probably indicate the manufacturing plant (either Arsenyev or Rostov); the next two denote the batch; and the last two are the production number proper. Thus this machine is the 84th Mi-24 built in the 75th batch.

73. An Mi-24VS crew photographed just prior to a sortie. Note the armour plating outside the cockpit. Most crews wear a bullet-proof vest for extra protection, and helmets of new design with protective ear flaps. The Afghan War sped the development of new clothing and equipment designed to make life safer for air crews.

72▲   73▼

74. A Polish Mi-24VE, 'White 74'. No UB-32 pods are fitted, but the sensors of the 'Natasha Device' are visible above the search/landing light. The first Polish Mi-24VEs entered service in about 1985 and the country now operates these in conjunction with its Mi-24Ds.

75. An Mi-24VE is checked out. The enlarged AT-6 guidance pod with black nose dome and the new searchlight are typical 'Hind-E' features, but there is no external difference between the Mi-24E and the high-altitude Mi-24V.

76. The WSO's console. The interior of the WSO's cockpit is chromate green, the console itself black. There is a first-aid kit box fitted on the starboard side; a second kit is installed in the pilot's cockpit.

77. Inside the passenger/cargo compartment of an Mi-24V; in the centre is the entranceway to the pilot's cockpit. The general interior finish is light grey.

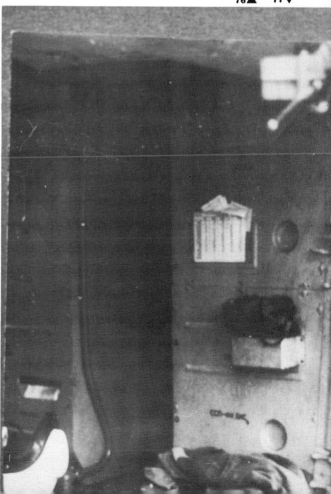

▲78 ▼79

78. Two ground crewmen loa
UPK-23 gunpod on an Mi-24V
The rear half of the pod
contains the ammunition
rounds, and the panels on th
forward section can be remov
for ease of maintenance to th
gun. The pod is silver with bl
stencilling. The UPK-23 hous
a twin-barrelled GSh-23L
cannon, good for use against
lightly armoured vehicles,
strongpoints and troop
concentrations and for air-to
combat with other helicopter
and slow-flying fixed-wing
aircraft. The mainwheel hub
bright olive green; the data o
the tyre reads '720=320'.

79. A Hungarian Mi-24VE
photographed over Budaörs,
summer 1986. This gunship i
armed with a single UB-32 po
on the inboard pylon, and a r
is fitted to accommodate a
further two 'Spiral' missiles.
such racks are carried on all
pylons, a total of twelve AT-6
can be loaded.

80. The Mi-24VE is also employed by the Czech Air Force in patrolling the West German border. For these sorties the helicopter is equipped with two 350-litre (77gal) fuel tanks on the outboard pylons. On such flights a 'Hind' may make contact with a helicopter from the West German *Bundesgrenzschutz* (Frontier Guard): here a Czech flight engineer is waving to one through an open window. (*Soldat und Technik*, via G. Lippert)

81. An Mi-35 'Hind-E', photographed at Kabul with a display of relevant weapons. On the stub-wing endplates are AT-6 'Spiral' missiles; a 80mm rocket pod hangs from the outboard pylon with a UPK-23 gunpod inboard. In the front, on the left, are 80mm rockets, whilst below the passenger entrance door are a pair of FAB 250 bombs, followed by what is probably a napalm canister. This photograph enables the comparative sizes of the 80mm and 57mm rockets to be appreciated. (W. Luczak)

82. An Mi-35 of the Afghan 377th Helicopter Regiment 'Hero of the Revolution'; 'Black 7' belongs to the flight commander. The Mi-35 is the export version of the Mi-24VE, and those operated by the Afghan Air Force are similar to the Soviet-operated Mi-24Es. This example has the Asian camouflage scheme of tan and medium green, with light blue undersurfaces. The national marking is of the type introduced in 1982.

80▲

81▲   82▼

▲83

▲84 ▼85

83. An Mi-24P captured by the camera during Exercise 'Friendship 82', when this new variant of the 'Hind' was first observed by the West and the ASCC reporting name 'Hind-F' allocated. The Mi-24P (for *Pushka*, or Cannon) has the 12.7mm gun deleted and a two-barrelled GSh-2-30 cannon fitted to the starboard side instead, its ammunition bay close by in the fuselage immediately above. This particular gunship is finished the Asian camouflage scheme

84. Two Soviet crewmen walk off from their gunship following a sortie; both men are wearing bullet-proof vests. The 'Hind' the left is Mi-24P 'Red 05' with an unusual camouflage pattern and several Mi-17s can be seen in the background. Both Mi-2 here carry the 80mm rocket pod.

85. Mi-24P 'Yellow 02', with two light grey drop tanks, 'engages' a number of T-72 tanks over an armour training ground. This 'Hind' is fitted with the new blade-type IFF antennas.

A pair of Mi-24Ps providing
port for Mi-8 troop
sports on the ground. The
2-30 is based on the GSh-
cannon, introduced in the
-21 and MiG-23 fighters; it
a rate of fire of 3,000 rounds
minute. This rate is possible
use the gun is designed on

the Gast principal first
developed in Germany in 1916:
the recoil of one barrel
automatically loads and fires the
other.

87. The latest known variant of
the 'Hind' is the electronic
warfare Mi-24 'Hind-G'. This

designation was first assigned to
the chemical-spraying version of
the Mi-24, but when it was
discovered that its tanks were
filled with fuel rather than
noxious agents the 'G' suffix was
reallocated. The 'Hind-G' has
been developed from the Mi-
24VE, but the LLLTV and

86▲

missile guidance pods have been
deleted; instead, a radome is
fitted on the port side, behind
the landing light. There is no
AT-6 launch equipment,
although rocket pods may be
carried. (*Soldat und Technik*,
via G. Lippert)

87▼

The *Fotofax* series

A new range of pictorial studies of military subjects for the modeller, historian and enthusiast. Each title features a carefully-selected set of photographs plus a data section of facts and figures on the topic covered. With line drawings and detailed captioning, every volume represents a succinct and valuable study of the subject. New and forthcoming titles:

Warbirds
F-111 Aardvark
P-47 Thunderbolt
B-52 Stratofortress
Stuka!
Jaguar
US Strategic Air Power:
  Europe 1942–1945
Dornier Bombers
RAF in Germany

Vintage Aircraft
German Naval Air Service
Sopwith Camel
Fleet Air Arm, 1920–1939
German Bombers of WWI

Soldiers
World War One: 1914
World War One: 1915
World War One: 1916
Union Forces of the American
  Civil War
Confederate Forces of the
  American Civil War
Luftwaffe Uniforms
British Battledress 1945–1967
  (2 vols)

Warships
Japanese Battleships, 1897–
  1945
Escort Carriers of World War
  Two
German Battleships, 1897–
  1945
Soviet Navy at War, 1941–1945
US Navy in World War Two,
  1943–1944
US Navy, 1946–1980 (2 vols)
British Submarines of World
  War One

Military Vehicles
The Chieftain Tank
Soviet Mechanized Firepower
  Today
British Armoured Cars since
  1945
NATO Armoured Fighting
  Vehicles
The Road to Berlin
NATO Support Vehicles

The *Illustrated* series

The internationally successful range of photo albums devoted current, recent and historic topics, compiled by leading autho and representing the best means of obtaining your own photo archive.

Warbirds
US Spyplanes
USAF Today
Strategic Bombers, 1945–1985
Air War over Germany
Mirage
US Naval and Marine Aircraft
  Today
USAAF in World War Two
B-17 Flying Fortress
Tornado
Junkers Bombers of World War
  Two
Argentine Air Forces in the
  Falklands Conflict
F-4 Phantom Vol II
Army Gunships in Vietnam
Soviet Air Power Today
F-105 Thunderchief
Fifty Classic Warbirds
Canberra and B-57
German Jets of World War Two

Vintage Warbirds
The Royal Flying Corps in
  World War One
German Army Air Service in
  World War One
RAF between the Wars
The Bristol Fighter
Fokker Fighters of World War
  One
Air War over Britain, 1914–
  1918
Nieuport Aircraft of World War
  One

Tanks
Israeli Tanks and Combat
  Vehicles
Operation Barbarossa
Afrika Korps
Self-Propelled Howitzers
British Army Combat Vehicles
  1945 to the Present
The Churchill Tank
US Mechanized Firepower
  Today
Hitler's Panzers
Panzer Armee Afrika
US Marine Tanks in World War
  Two

Warships
The Royal Navy in 1980s
The US Navy Today
NATO Navies of the 1980s
British Destroyers in World
  War Two
Nuclear Powered Submarine
Soviet Navy Today
British Destroyers in World
  War One
The World's Aircraft Carrier
  1914–1945
The Russian Convoys, 1941–
  1945
The US Navy in World War
  Two
British Submarines in Worl
  War Two
British Cruisers in World W
  One
U-Boats of World War Two
Malta Convoys, 1940–1943

Uniforms
US Special Forces of World
  War Two
US Special Forces 1945 to t
  Present
The British Army in Northe
  Ireland
Israeli Defence Forces, 1948
  the Present
British Special Forces, 1945
  Present
US Army Uniforms Europe,
  1944–1945
The French Foreign Legion
Modern American Soldier
Israeli Elite Units
US Airborne Forces of Worl
  War Two
The Boer War
The Commandos World War
  Two to the Present
Victorian Colonial Wars

A catalogue listing these series and other Arms & Armour Press titles is available on request from: Sales Department, Arms & Armour Press, Artillery House, Artillery Row, London SW1P 1RT.